HELPING SOMEONE OVERCOME ADDICTION

VOLUME I:
WHAT IS ADDICTION?

BY
GARY W. SMITH
CERTIFIED CHEMICAL DEPENDENCY COUNSELOR
EXECUTIVE DIRECTOR, NARCONON OF OKLAHOMA, INC.
AND
DERRY HALLMARK
CERTIFIED CHEMICAL DEPENDENCY COUNSELOR
SENIOR DIRECTOR FOR EXPANSION, NARCONON OF OKLAHOMA, INC.

NARCONON®
ARROWHEAD

Important Note

In reading this book, be very certain you never go past a word you do not fully understand.

The only reason a person gives up a study or becomes confused or unable to learn is because he or she has gone past a word that was not understood.

The confusion or inability to grasp or learn comes AFTER a word that the person did not have defined and understood.

Have you ever had the experience of coming to the end of a page and realizing you didn't know what you had read? Well, somewhere earlier on that page you went past a word that you had no definition for or an incorrect definition for.

Here's an example. "It was found that when the crepuscle arrived the children were quieter and when it was not present, they were much livelier." You see what happens. You think you don't understand the whole idea, but the inability to understand came entirely from the one word you could not define, *crepuscle*, which means twilight or darkness.

It may not only be the new and unusual words that you will have to look up. Some commonly used words can often be misdefined and so cause confusion.

This datum about not going past an undefined word is the most important fact in the whole subject of study. Every subject you have taken up and abandoned had its words which you failed to get defined.

Therefore, in studying this book be very, very certain you never go past a word you do not fully understand. If the material becomes confusing or you can't seem to grasp it, there will be a word just earlier that you have not understood. Don't go any farther, but go back to BEFORE you got into trouble, find the misunderstood word and get it defined.

Definitions

As an aid to the reader, words most likely to be misunderstood have been defined in footnotes the first time they occur in the text. Words sometimes have several meanings. The footnote definitions in this book give only the meaning that the word has as it is used in the text. Other definitions for the word can be found in a dictionary.

A glossary including all the footnote definitions is at the back of this book.

CONTENTS

The authors of this text
gratefully acknowledge
L. Ron Hubbard
for his gift to Narconon
of his revolutionary
research and developments
in the field of drug rehabilitation.

"Helping Someone Overcome Addiction"
is based on his works.

WHAT IS HELP?

WHAT IS HELP?

Drug addiction is a powerful and destructive force that rips families apart and ruins the lives of good people every day.

Though the person who uses drugs suffers immensely, the people in the drug user's life who love them often suffer just as much or more. This is not usually because of the obvious reasons, such as the bad things the drug user has done to those who love them.

The greatest suffering for those who love the drug user is almost always the helpless feeling of not knowing what to do to keep the person from destroying his or her life with drugs.

Help generally means to aid, to support, to relieve, to prevent, etc. This is exactly what someone with a loved one abusing drugs and alcohol is attempting to do: to aid them in quitting drugs, to support their ability to stay alive, to prevent them from suffering more or prevent them from completely destroying themselves with the use of drugs.

Usually, those individuals who love and care for someone who is addicted to drugs and alcohol have the willingness to help the person get off drugs, but often lack the knowledge of what it is they are confronting. They don't fully understand addiction. Therefore, many efforts to cause the drug user to get better or quit drugs are not successful. When these attempts fail, a feeling of hopelessness and helplessness often results.

Author and humanitarian L. Ron Hubbard defines "failure" as: "...the inability to handle that which has been started after that course of action is entered."

A common example of the failure encountered by someone helping a loved one addicted to drugs and alcohol would be a brother who decides that he is going to help his sister stop killing herself, and those who love her, with her drug use.

He reasons with his sister, threatens her and does literally everything in his power to get her to simply "see the light."

The sister agrees and says she'll never use drugs again. The brother believes her and feels great that he was able to help her.

The next evening the sister doesn't come home at the expected time. As a matter of fact, she doesn't come home all night.

In the morning when she does come home, it is very obvious by her appearance and actions that she has been using drugs again. The brother gets mad and is disappointed, but often he will be more disturbed by his utter failure to cause[1] her to quit using drugs.

Each time this happens, the brother will sink lower and lower into the feelings of helplessness and hopelessness. He fears that he will never be able to save his sister and may even finally decide to just give up.

To watch someone kill themselves slowly with drugs and alcohol and feel unable to help them recover is one of the most miserable ways that a person can spend his or her existence.

This educational series is designed to assist the loved ones of drug users in their primary goal: to HELP.

---

[1]**cause** - to make happen or occur; to be the origin of something.

The first step in assisting someone with a problem such as drug use and abuse is to understand what the actual problem is. It is very difficult, if not impossible, for someone to solve a problem if they don't understand what the problem is that they are trying to solve.

With this in mind, we have assembled this first book in the *Helping Someone Overcome Addiction* series into distinct, easy to understand sections so that anyone can KNOW exactly what drug addiction really is and, therefore, be able to successfully HELP someone overcome it.

Later volumes will fully explain what the drug user and his or her loved ones need to do to rid themselves of addiction.

Addiction CAN be overcome. With a complete understanding of addiction and the proper tools to apply, virtually anyone can rid themselves of the harmful effects of drugs and alcohol and lead a productive drug-free life. It is with this purpose in mind that the following materials are presented.

DRUGS DEFINED

DRUGS DEFINED

In order to understand drug addiction, it is important to understand what a drug is. In medical terms, a drug is any substance that when taken into the body may modify one or more of its functions. A simpler definition, given by L. Ron Hubbard, whose research and breakthroughs in drug rehabilitation are utilized in the Narconon® drug and alcohol rehabilitation program[2], is:

"Drugs are essentially poisons[3]. The degree they are taken determines the effect. A small amount acts as a stimulant[4]. A greater amount acts as a sedative[5]. A larger amount acts as a poison and can kill one dead. This is true of any drug. Each has a different amount at which it gives those results."

A small amount acts as a stimulant.

A greater amount acts as a sedative.

A larger amount acts as a poison and can kill one dead.

[2]**Narconon® drug and alcohol rehabilitation program -** a non-traditional residential drug and alcohol rehabilitation program. Over 70% of Narconon program graduates remain drug-free.
[3]**poison -** any substance that causes injury or illness or death of a living organism.
[4]**stimulant -** a drug that temporarily quickens some physiological* process.
*physiological** - of or consistent with an organism's normal functioning.

For example, if you look in a standard dictionary today for the word "drug" you will find a definition like this:

"a substance that treats or prevents or provides relief from the symptoms of disease."

However, we can track ancient Greek and Roman definitions of drugs with their full derivations[6]: *pharmakon* in Greek and *venenum* in Latin, and find quite a different definition.

Pharmakon[7], which gives us the word "pharmacy", "pharmacological" and related words, means both medication and poison.

Hippocrates
"The Father of Medicine"
~470 B.C. - 410 B.C.

Venenum[8], which gives us the word "venom," translates into drug, potion and poison.

In both the Greek and Roman civilizations, the common view of drugs is that they were both medications and poisons.

[5]**sedative -** a drug that reduces excitability and calms a person.
[6]**derivation -** an explanation of the historical origins of a word or phrase
[7] 1913 Webster's Unabridged Dictionary
[8] Notre Dame Online Latin Translator

"Intoxicate" is derived from "toxic."

The word "toxic" is derived from the Greek word *toxikon*[9], a poison for arrows. Toxic is defined as "poisonous" so to intoxicate someone would thus mean to poison him.

Today when we use the word "intoxicated," we are generally describing someone who is under the influence of some substance, usually alcohol, but it could be any drug.

[9] 1913 Webster's Unabridged Dictionary

Today, instead of calling a drug poisonous we just talk about its "side effects[10]."

The United States Food and Drug Administration states that there is no drug that does not produce side effects[11] and that those side effects often emerge long after a drug has been approved and released for public sale and use[12].

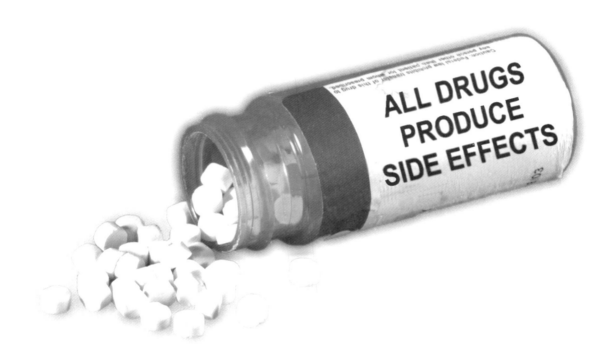

In the case of medical use of prescribed drugs, side effects are produced, but often the beneficial effects of these medications, when used as directed, outweigh any negative side effects that they cause.

[10]**side effect** - a secondary and usually adverse (undesirable) effect of a drug or therapy.
[11] U.S. Food and Drug Administration Consumer magazine: July- August 2002
[12] U.S. Department of Health and Human Services, Food and Drug Administration, May 1999

The term "side effect" also applies to addiction. In this case, the harm of the side effects far outweighs any physical or mental good that the drug may do. People never start or continue with drug use desiring to destroy their bodies, their ability to function in life, their family and everything else in life they care about. But, these physically and emotionally devastating "side effects" commonly accompany the use and abuse of drugs.

NUTRITIONAL DEFICIENCIES AND ADDICTION

NUTRITIONAL DEFICIENCIES AND ADDICTION

One of the first poisonous or destructive side effects that drugs have on any individual is the burning up or reduction of the nutritional stores in the body.

Vitamins[13], minerals[14] and amino acids[15] are the actual fuel that the body needs to properly function and to repair itself.

Taking drugs accelerates the burning up of these nutrients[16]. It is partially the rapid consumption and depletion of these nutrients that helps to create a totally artificial sense of well-being while under the influence of the drug.

For instance, as the body burns up the B vitamins and others, the person feels temporarily better and this adds to the euphoric[17] feeling the drug creates.

---

[13]**vitamins -** any of a group of organic* substances essential to normal metabolism.
[14]**mineral -** an inorganic** element, such as calcium, used in the metabolism of human beings, animals and plants.
*organic -** of or relating to or derived from living organisms.
inorganic - lacking the properties characteristic of living organisms.
[15]**amino acid -** organic compounds which combine to form proteins.
[16]**nutrient -** any substance that can be metabolized by an organism to give energy and build tissue.
[17]**euphoric -** characterized by an exaggerated feeling of well-being or happiness.

This same process of burning up the nutrients in the body and the resulting nutritional deficiencies[18] cause cellular damage often leading to discomfort, pain, disease, and unfortunately, the need for more drugs.

It is well documented that drugs, both pharmaceutical and "street drugs"– called "controlled substances" such as cocaine[19], heroin[20], etc – frequently cause deficiencies in vitamins B_1, B_2, B_3, B_6, B_{12}, C, D and K. They also create shortages in biotin, folic acid, phosphorous, calcium, magnesium, iron, acidophilus, potassium, coenzyme Q10, zinc and other essential nutrients.

Not all drugs cause deficiencies in all these different vitamins, minerals, and amino acids, but all drugs do cause the depletion and possible deficiency in at least some of them.

[18]**deficiency** - lack of an adequate quantity or number; the state of needing something that is absent or unavailable.
[19]**cocaine** - a powerfully addictive stimulant that directly affects the brain.
 (from National Institute on Drug Abuse (NIDA), a part of the National Institutes of Health, a component of the U.S. Department of Health and Human Services.)
[20]**heroin** - a highly addictive narcotic derived from the opium poppy plant.
 (from NIDA)

VITAMIN AND MINERAL DEFINITIONS
(from National Institutes of Health)

Vitamin B$_1$ (Thiamine) - helps the body cells convert carbohydrates into energy. It is also essential for the functioning of the heart and for healthy nerve cells and the brain.

Vitamin B$_2$ (Riboflavin) - works with the other B vitamins and is important for body growth and red cell production. Similar to thiamine, it helps in releasing energy from carbohydrates.

Vitamin B$_3$ (Niacin) - is a water-soluble B vitamin important in energy metabolism.

Vitamin B$_6$ (Pyroxidine) - helps in the formation of red blood cells and in the maintenance of normal brain function.

Vitamin B$_{12}$ - is important for metabolism. It helps in the formation of red blood cells and in the maintenance of the central nervous system[21].

Vitamin C - promotes healthy teeth and gums, helps in the absorption of iron, and helps maintain normal connective tissue. It also promotes wound healing.

Vitamin D - promotes the body's absorption of calcium, which is essential for the normal development of healthy teeth and bones. It also helps maintain adequate blood levels of calcium and phosphorus, which are minerals.

Vitamin K - is known as the clotting vitamin, because without it blood would not coagulate. Some studies indicate that it helps in maintaining strong bones in older people.

---

[21]**nervous system -** the sensory and control apparatus, consisting of a network of nerve cells, that regulates the body's responses to input, especially from the environment.

Biotin - is essential for the metabolism of proteins and carbohydrates, and in the synthesis of hormones and cholesterol.

Folic acid - works with vitamin B12 in the production of red blood cells. It is necessary for the synthesis of DNA, which controls heredity as well as tissue growth and cell function.

Phosphorus - aids in the formation of the bones and teeth. It plays an important role in the body's utilization of carbohydrates and fats, and in the synthesis of protein for the growth, maintenance, and repair of cells and tissues.

Calcium - is a mineral important for strong teeth and bones and for muscle and nerve function.

Magnesium - is a mineral necessary in many metabolic processes. It helps nerves and muscles function properly.

Iron - is a mineral that is an essential constituent of blood and muscle and that is important for the transport of oxygen.

Acidophilus - bacteria found in yogurt that help restore a supportive bacterial environment to an intestinal tract affected by disease and antibiotics.

Potassium - is one of the minerals responsible for maintaining the electrical stability of the cells of your heart and nervous system. Potassium is important for cell and muscle growth, and it plays a major role in maintaining normal fluid balance.

Coenzyme Q10 - helps cells to produce energy, and it acts as an antioxidant. It has shown an ability to stimulate the immune system and to protect the heart from certain types of damage.

Zinc - is a mineral involved in wound healing, sense of taste and smell, growth and sexual maturation and is contained in enzymes that regulate metabolism.

These drug induced nutritional deficiencies are easily observed when someone uses marijuana[22]. Marijuana burns through one's vitamins and minerals while numbing the central nervous system.

While quickly creating a false sense of cheerfulness, marijuana creates in the body an overwhelming desire for food, which some people call "the munchies."

What has happened is that the user's vitamins and minerals have been burned up and the body is craving them, so the urge to eat is actually the result of the reduction of some of the body's building blocks — the vitamins, minerals and amino acids.

[22]**marijuana -** a drug consisting of the dried leaves of the hemp plant; smoked or chewed for euphoric effect

Eventually, the effect of the drug wears off. At this point the person actually feels much worse than he or she did before the drug was taken.

This is because the person's body no longer has the basic fuels it needs to carry on normal operations. Physically, the user feels tired, "hung over," run down and out of energy. This may be mild or severe, depending on how toxic the drug is that he or she is using, but the change is always for the worse.

As the person continues to use drugs, his or her physical condition becomes worse and worse. Because of the shortage of vitamins, minerals and amino acids that the body needs to function well, illness becomes common.

The following are just some of the conditions that can occur as a result of drug-induced nutritional deficiency:

CONDITIONS INDUCED BY NUTRITIONAL DEFICIENCIES

anemia - a condition in which the blood is deficient in red blood cells, in hemoglobin, or in total volume; lack of vitality.

depression - an emotional state often characterized by sadness, inactivity, difficulty in thinking and concentration, a significant increase or decrease in appetite and time spent sleeping, feelings of hopelessness, and sometimes suicidal tendencies.

fatigue - weariness or exhaustion from labor, exertion, or stress.

weakness - the quality or state of being weak; also: an instance or period of being weak.

birth defects - a physical or biochemical defect that is present at birth and may be inherited or environmentally induced.

heart disease - an abnormal organic condition of the heart or of the heart and circulation.

high blood pressure - abnormally high blood pressure and especially arterial blood pressure; also, the systemic condition accompanying high blood pressure.

asthma - a condition that is marked by continuous or spasmodic labored breathing accompanied by wheezing, by a sense of constriction in the chest, and often by attacks of coughing or gasping.

osteoporosis - a condition that affects especially older women and is characterized by decrease in bone mass with decreased density and enlargement of bone spaces producing fragility.

cramps - a painful involuntary spasmodic contraction of a muscle.

tooth decay - decomposition of the teeth.

anxiety - a vague unpleasant emotion that is experienced in anticipation of some (usually poorly defined) misfortune

These nutritional deficiencies can create a condition where an addict's body no longer has a fully-functioning immune system[23] to fight off diseases and infections. So he or she never really feels healthy anymore. The only time that addicts think they feel healthy (or at least no longer feel ill due to the nutritional deficiencies present because of drug use) is when they are actually USING and

are under the influence of the painkilling effects of drugs.

The person takes the drug and feels good. Since the user feels good, he or she assumes that their body is also healthy. No one likes pain and discomfort, and we all instinctively try to avoid these feelings. This thought process reinforces a drug user's desire to take more drugs, while the physical condition of the addict is actually going downhill and progressively getting worse.

[23]**immune system -** a system that protects the body from foreign substances and disease-causing organisms by producing the immune response.

In time, as the person uses any drug, his or her body will begin to adapt to the presence of these toxic chemicals. The body, in effect, gets used to having the chemicals in it. The adaptation of the body to chemicals is called tolerance[24].

People's tolerance to a drug will increase the longer they use the substance. As the tolerance builds, the euphoric effects they started taking the drug for in the first place become less and less the more and longer they use it. They compulsively try to achieve the same good feelings the drug once gave them by taking more and more of the drug. It's a vicious circle.

In the beginning, users experience an intense feeling of well-being or a "high" when they first use the drug. As the addict's body increases its tolerance to these chemicals, the intensity of the "highs" they are seeking lessens and the physical and mental "lows" that they feel when they come down intensify. These "lows" are driven by nutritional deficiencies that eventually result in a declining state of health and a constant state of physical and mental discomfort that become increasingly apparent to the addict each time the painkilling effects of the drug wear off. As the addict's physical condition worsens, they use larger amounts of the drug to handle the growing level of pain.

At this stage of addiction, the individual is prone to overdose. The body's tolerance to the drug masks the poisoning effects of the larger and more lethal amounts of the drug that the addict needs to take to kill the physical pain or dicomfort that exists when they are not under the influence of the drug.

[24]**tolerance -** the power or capacity of an organism to withstand, and function in, unfavorable environmental conditions.

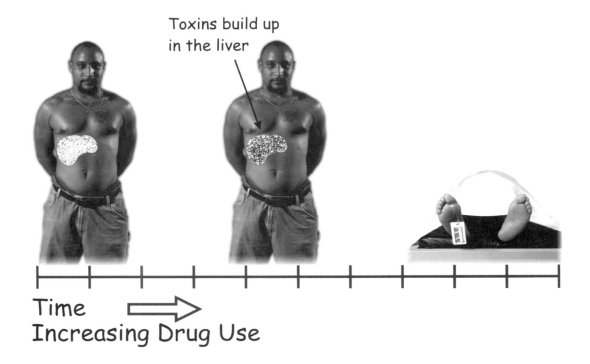

Toxins build up
in the liver

Time
Increasing Drug Use

As the amount of drugs taken increases, the physical damage done to the addict's body becomes greater as well.

There are hundreds of less-visible signs of the damage done to a drug user's body. The list is long. Liver and kidney problems, damage to the heart, brain damage and even the onset of diabetes are some common, well-documented results of abusing drugs.

Any time users decide to stop taking drugs, they feel the damage they have done to themselves and their bodies. Once off the drug, a whole variety of physical problems become apparent to these individuals. Commonly, they may feel ill, experience a lack of energy or suffer aches or pains that are not present when the user is under the influence of drugs.

Sadly, this constantly reminds the user that to "feel good" they should use the drug again. For example, if a person stops using cocaine or methamphetamine[25], he or she may have headaches from lack of vitamins, be tired all the time and feel the need to start using the drug again just to have energy and get rid of the pain. Withdrawal[26] from any drug will have a similar effect.

This presents a problem. Drug users hope they can quit drugs and live a normal life. However, when they attempt to stop, they have no energy and feel bad all the time. They naturally want to feel good and not feel sick. As they are unaware of the actual nutritional causes of the way they feel and have no alternative method of handling the problem they are caught in the trap of having to go back on the drug or suffer through life without it.

Fully handling nutritional deficiencies is vital to effective drug rehabilitation.

[25]**methamphetamine -** a powerfully addictive stimulant that affects the central nervous system.
(from NIDA)
[26]**withdrawal -** the physiological and mental symptoms that accompany the stopping of taking an addictive drug.

DRUGS BLOCK THE SENSES AND PERCEPTIONS

DRUGS BLOCK THE SENSES AND PERCEPTIONS

Many drugs block the senses and perceptions[27] by numbing the central nervous system. This prevents the person from experiencing the world around them, but also prevents the person from experiencing internal pain and discomfort, which is the body's warning signs that an internal problem needs to be addressed.

As we will see, the numbing of the person's perception, both internally and externally, will not only prove to be harmful and in some cases deadly, but will also strongly trap a person in the vicious cycle of addiction.

[27]**perception** - becoming aware of something via the senses.

INTERNAL PERCEPTION

The internal numbing effect that drugs produce prevents the person from experiencing physical pain and discomfort.

Covering up or masking pain and discomfort is one of the most common reasons the medical community prescribes drugs to patients in the first place.

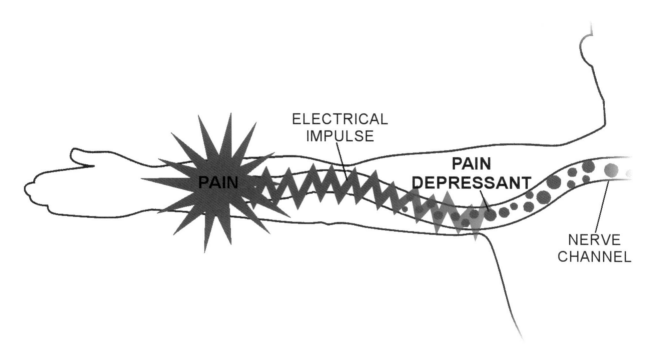

Unfortunately, this same action of blocking or numbing the pain and discomfort of life can create the breeding ground for illness, disease and addiction.

There are many drugs that block the nervous system's ability to communicate real pain and discomfort messages from different parts of the body; however, these warnings are intended to alert the person so that the cause of the problem can be located and handled.

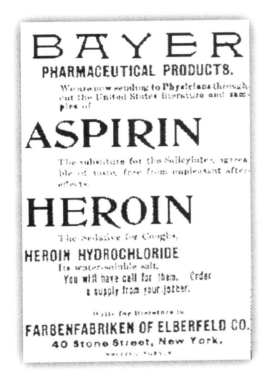

1897 Bayer Heroin Ad

These drugs are either prescription drugs prescribed by a doctor, "over the counter" or non-prescription drugs bought in stores, or illegal drugs sold on the street by criminal drug dealers.

Remember that many illegal drugs were originally synthesized or discovered and manufactured by pharmaceutical companies as prescription drugs.

**Cocaine Toothache Drops
Advertisement, 1885**

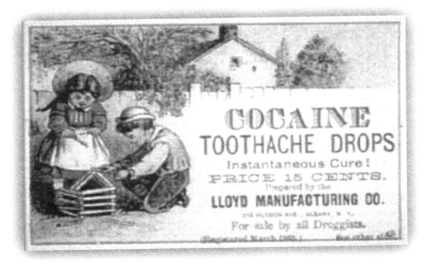

While prescription and non-prescription drugs often seem helpful when a person suffers a major painful injury, with continued use they have negative effects due to the same sense-dulling properties that make them useful.

By constantly blocking the body's internal warning signs called pain and discomfort, the person can allow real physical problems to grow out of control before detection.

The drug user can often be dreadfully sick, yet be utterly unaware of the illness due to the numbing effects of the drugs.

As the drug user is unaware of these negative physical conditions the person often does not get the proper medical help they need.

The end result is a continually worsening physical condition and, in some cases, disease-related death.

A prime example of this downward spiral is the case of cirrhosis[28] of the liver, commonly caused by alcohol abuse. An alcoholic is often unable to feel the many warning signs of the damage being done to their liver until it is too late to remedy easily.

A more common "over-the-counter" drug example of this damaging process is that of aspirin, which is often taken for the symptoms of a headache.

Aspirin doesn't actually "cure" a headache. Aspirin simply "short-circuits" the person's ability to get the pain messages coming from the cause of the headache. The nutritional deficiency or physical problem that originally CAUSED the headache is still there, but is simply no longer PERCEIVED by the person taking the aspirin.

[28]**cirrhosis -** a chronic disease interfering with the normal functioning of the liver; the primary cause is chronic alcoholism.

Frequently, when the drug wears off, the headache returns and may be more severe because the original problem has become worse as it was masked or hidden and not directly addressed or handled.

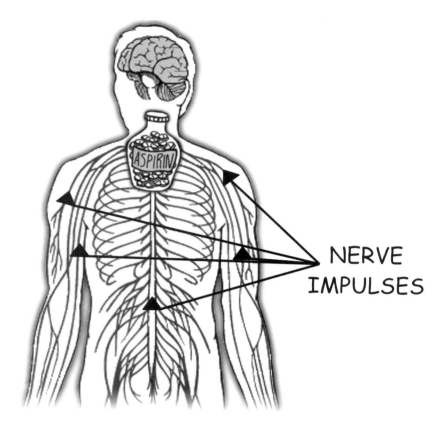

NERVE IMPULSES

Drug users damage their bodies by depriving them of food and nutrition. This creates nutritional deficiencies and then masks the warning signs of these problems with the very effects that the drug use creates.

The person's physical condition becomes worse and worse. As this occurs, the same person will use more and more drugs in an attempt at "handling" the pain and discomfort that accompanies the condition. The more drugs the person uses, the worse their physical condition becomes.

This is a very destructive cycle that will either end in death or the abstinence[29] from drugs.

---

[29]**abstinence** - the act or practice of refraining* from indulging** an appetite
*refraining - not doing something, resisting.
**indulging - enjoying to excess; giving satisfaction to.

EXTERNAL PERCEPTION

As for external perception, drug use causes people to lose their ability to perceive the world around them, making them a hazard to themselves and others.

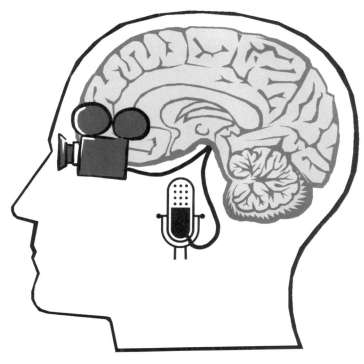

We experience the world around us through sensory channels such as smell, sight, touch, hearing and taste. These sensory channels are like the microphone and camera lens of our mind's video camera that receive the sensations[30] and perceptions we use to handle our environment and function in day to day life.

The ability to know that dinner is being prepared by sensing the aroma of cooking food, or the recognition that there is something wrong with a baby in the next room by hearing the sound of crying, are some of the ways we survive and handle our environment.

[30]**sensation -** the faculty through which the external world is perceived and understood.

A mother who has lost her ability to hear may not know her baby is in severe pain because she can't hear the baby's cries.

A person whose vision is impaired is at risk from oncoming traffic each time he or she crosses the street.

When drugs are used, the central nervous system becomes numbed or slowed and the normal sensory inputs are blocked. This occurs primarily due to overstimulation of the nervous system when stimulants are used or deadening of the senses when depressants[31] are used.

Without the ability to sense the environment a person can become a great danger to themselves and others around them.

---

[31]**depressant -** capable of depressing physiological or psychological activity or response by a chemical agent.

The most common and horrifying example of this negative effect and consequence of drug use is the drunk driver. We know all too well the story of a person driving while intoxicated, who then loses control of their vehicle and kills innocent people as a result.

While there are obviously well-publicized tragedies associated with the numbing effects drugs produce, there are untold numbers of lesser-known but damaging problems this "side effect" is responsible for.

Problems at work such as poor job performance due to slow response time or frequent mistakes or accidents can and do occur regularly. Other problems include neglect of child care, sexual inability, car accidents, property damage, poor school performance and thousands of other very real and damaging consequences which commonly occur due to this disconnection from the environment created by the dulling of the body's sensory channels.

The drug user desires to function normally in life and to be able to handle their physical environment.

Unfortunately, by using drugs this same individual robs him or herself of the sensory information required to operate successfully. Consequently, the drug user makes mistakes, causes problems, and is generally unable to handle the environment and his or her own life.

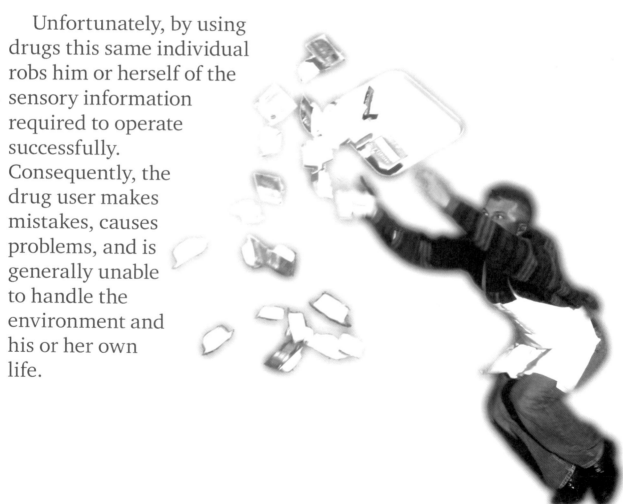

When the drug user becomes addicted to the drugs they use, they feel bad or ashamed of their own inability to function normally in life and this, too, is a problem.

The person will usually try many things in an attempt at solving this problem, but often will resort to the same temporary "solution" which caused these problems in the first place — more drugs.

The simple truth is that drugs are essentially poisons. The effects that drugs have on both the individual and his or her body are gruesome and cruel.

Drugs deprive the body of the nutrition it needs to operate properly, causing disease and dysfunction. Drugs are a no-win game.

Drugs are never the solution to problems, if only because they create far more problems than they could ever hope to solve.

PROBLEMS DEFINED

PROBLEMS DEFINED

Alcohol and addictive drugs are basically painkillers. They mask physical or emotional pain and alter the mind's perception of reality. They make people numb.

For drugs to be attractive to a person there must first be some underlying unhappiness, sense of hopelessness, or physical pain. These negative emotions, feelings and sensations are "problems" for the person, as they don't want to feel or experience them.

The problem the person is having seems overwhelming and a solution is not readily available to them. If this person attempts to solve his or her problems with drugs and alcohol, he or she is beginning what, for many, becomes the cycle of addiction.

Before we attempt to unravel the problem of addiction, we must first understand the actual definition of the word "problem" as well as take a look at what having a problem means.

L. Ron Hubbard defines a "problem" as "the conflict arising from two opposing intentions"…"it's one thing versus another thing"… "It's intention versus counter-intention that worries the person."

Intention is defined as: "an act of intending; an idea or action that you intend to carry out."

Counter-intention then is an intention, or idea one is going to do something which is counter to or against another intention.

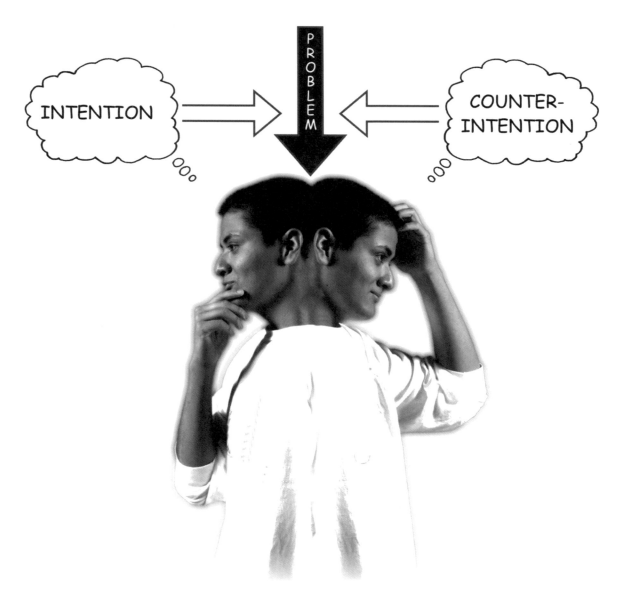

Sometimes, people have the idea that if they lose weight they will feel better about themselves. Therefore, they have an intention to go on a diet and lose weight.

They also like eating a lot of sweets and enjoy the way they feel when they eat these foods. They also have the intention, therefore, of eating a lot of sweets.

Assuming that eating a lot of sweets is not the best way to lose weight, then we can easily assume that this could be a problem for these individuals.

L. Ron Hubbard further defines a problem as follows:

"You've got two forces or two ideas that are interlocked of comparable magnitude[32]"…"the first consequence of a problem is indecision[33]".

In the previous example, the two opposing intentions of intending to go on a diet and losing weight, but also intending to eat fattening food, will often create a state of confusion. The person wants to lose weight and feel better about him or herself, but also constantly desires fattening food to eat. The person is torn between two desires and cannot easily figure out what to do.

[32]**magnitude** - greatness, in reference to influence or effect.
[33]**indecision** - doubt concerning two or more possible alternatives or courses of action.

There are many obvious examples of everyday problems which a person encounters while living life. Sometimes the difficulty in resolving these problems seems overwhelming and the consequences of not resolving them can be catastrophic[34]. For someone who is struggling with a problem such as addiction, the person's life may literally depend on finding and implementing a workable solution.

So with the definition of a problem in mind, we can now look at the problem of drug use and abuse.

PHYSICAL INJURY

DIFFICULTY FITTING IN

BOREDOM

We start off with an individual who is basically good. This person develops a pain or discomfort that he or she does not know how to resolve or cannot confront[35]. This could be a physical discomfort such as an injury or chronic pain. It can also include problems such as having difficulty "fitting in" as a child or a teenager, anxiety[36] due to peer[37] pressure, or as is often the case with young people, shyness or even boredom.

[34]**catastrophic** - extremely harmful, bringing physical or financial ruin.
[35]**confront -** to deal with (something unpleasant) directly, without fear or uncertainty .
[36]**anxiety -** a vague, unpleasant emotion experienced in anticipation of some (usually poorly defined) misfortune.
[37]**peer -** a person who is of equal standing with another in a group.

Persons experiencing these types of pain or discomfort have a real problem. They feel that their present situation is unbearable and see no good solution to the problems they face.

Everyone has experienced problems like these in life to a greater or lesser degree. The difference between an addict and a non-addict is that addicts choose drugs or alcohol as a solution to their unwanted problems or discomforts, and progressively adopt drug or alcohol use as a common solution to other problems they become faced with in the future.

The person tries drugs or alcohol. The drugs or alcohol APPEAR to solve the person's immediate problem, and he or she believes they feel better.

The person now has a false sense or perception that he or she is better able to deal with life so the drugs have become valuable to them.

The person looks on drugs or alcohol as a cure for unwanted feelings. The painkilling effects of drugs or alcohol become a solution to the person's discomfort.

This release from his or her problem has value[38], and is the main reason the person uses drugs or drinks a second or third time. They have the idea that using drugs or alcohol solved problems before, so using them again should be able to solve problems again. With this pattern of constantly trying to solve life's problems with drugs and alcohol, it can be just a matter of time before he or she becomes fully addicted and loses the ability to control drug or alcohol use.

[38]**value** - the quality (positive or negative) that renders something desirable or valuable.

Drug addiction, then, results from excessive or continued use of mentally or physically habit-forming drugs in an attempt to resolve the underlying symptoms of discomfort, pain or unhappiness.

There are many examples of how drugs could be considered valuable and a solution to a person's problem.

Example 1

A teenager desires to be loved and trusted by his family and also really wants to fit in with the popular crowd and be liked by his peers. This peer group also uses alcohol and other drugs, so in order to "fit in," he would also need to use alcohol and other drugs.

This is what is commonly refered to as peer pressure.

There is not always pressure exerted by the members of the group. The individual's desire to be in agreement with others and fit in creates pressure on the person to follow the group's behaviors. As these two intentions, wanting to please his family, and wanting to be popular, are seemingly counter to each other, this person has a very common problem. By using drugs he is in agreement with his friends, and the drugs also temporarily remove the guilt feelings stemming from his doing actions which displease the family. The drugs seem to solve this problem.

Intention to
fit in with friends
and use drugs

Intention to be
loved and trusted
by family

Example 2

A husband is having trouble at home. For various reasons, he and his wife fight and argue, but he does not have the ability to confront or to communicate with her and work out their problems. He feels he is under an extreme amount of constant emotional stress and sees no way out. He desires to continue the marriage, but equally desires to not be angry and upset all the time. He doesn't want to feel this way day after day, but cannot seem to resolve the conflicts he is having with his wife. Drugs numb and lessen the pain temporarily and seem to offer a solution to his problem.

Example 3

The following is a simple example that is often overlooked. A young girl finds herself unchallenged at home and at school. She wants to be a good daughter and make her parents proud of her, but her daily chores and duties lack any adventure or excitement. She is bored. She has an intention to be a good person and do what she knows is right, but she also has an intention to become involved in something EXCITING to break the monotony[39] she feels in life.

There are some other kids at school that use drugs and she knows that this is dangerous, but the idea of taking a risk is much more exciting than her current situation. The adventure of taking drugs is a solution to her problem of boredom.

---

[39]**monotony** - the quality of boring sameness and lack of variety.

The truth in these examples, and in millions more, is that the person actually didn't start out wanting to take drugs. It was only when he or she attempted to solve a problem that using drugs became an option. Due to overwhelming mass-marketing[40] campaigns, entertainment which carries a pro-drug message, and other related environmental misinformation[41], drugs are heavily promoted as offering an immediate solution to all problems.

[40]**mass-marketing -** the act or business of promoting sales of a product to a large number of people, as by advertising or packaging.
[41]**misinformation -** information that is incorrect.

The teenager who deeply desires to be popular and the husband who desires to be married, but also wants to feel at peace with his daily surroundings – both have the exact same problem at a fundamental[42] level. Neither the boy nor the husband can see anything wrong with either intention they have. Unfortunately, they also found a temporary solution to their problems by the use of drugs.

Obviously none of the individuals mentioned earlier made a conscious[43] decision to become addicted to drugs. Drugs weren't even part of the problem they were trying to solve. Nevertheless, the solution they chose can easily lead to the trap of addiction.

As people continue using drugs and alcohol to solve problems, they create new and larger problems that they will probably end up attempting to solve with the same solutions they have used in the past: drugs.

[42]**fundamental** - serving as an essential component; involving basic facts or principles.
[43]**conscious** - intentionally conceived; having awareness of surroundings and sensations and thoughts.

If the person feels tired, he or she will use a drug or alcohol to give themselves energy. If the person feels depressed he or she will use a drug or alcohol to feel more upbeat. If the person feels uncomfortable with people, he or she will use drugs or alcohol to make themselves feel more socially acceptable.

There are hundreds or thousands of "problems" that a person might attempt to solve by using drugs or alcohol. The truth is that these problems are actually NOT solved by the use of drugs or alcohol. These problems are only masked temporarily and the real underlying problems that drugs were intended to solve remain untouched and unhandled.

This is the lie that comes with the use of drugs.

As you will see throughout this entire book, problems and wrong solutions are at the core of every piece of the addiction puzzle.

As the drug and alcohol user begins to use more drugs and alcohol, the drugs and alcohol themselves begin to create problems for the user.

The rest of this series explains the actual mechanical traps drugs and alcohol create for the unsuspecting person caught using them. Anyone interested in helping someone overcome addiction will need to be fully familiar with these traps of addiction so as to actually understand how to help the person regain his or her life and freedom. Nothing could be more honorable or necessary in today's world.

DRUG CRAVINGS AND RELAPSE

DRUG CRAVINGS[44] AND RELAPSE[45]

When we say that a person has drug cravings what is meant is that, despite the person knowing that using drugs is not OK, he or she will continually find themselves desiring to use drugs and remembering times they have used drugs in the past.

The experience of craving drugs is sometimes just a passing thought of using drugs by the person during a busy day. Sometimes the drug craving can seem like an overwhelming, unstoppable urge that only the use of more drugs can satisfy.

[44]**craving -** an intense desire for some particular thing. consuming desire.
[45]**relapse -** failure to maintain a higher state.

In either case, drug cravings are the leading cause of relapse for a person who is desperately trying to leave drugs behind. Fighting these daily or hourly desires to use drugs is a humiliating and frustrating battle for those who seek to quit drugs. The process of craving drugs can literally go on for the remainder of the drug user's life if the cause of the drug craving is not completely handled.

A person craving drugs isn't quite tracking or following with what is going on around them. They can be in the same room with you, looking like they are doing the same things you are doing, but actually, they are only partially there.

Some part of the drug user's attention is constantly being pulled away from the present environment and placed on past drug related experiences. This can be slight, as when the person is seen to make occasional mistakes, or it can be as serious as total insanity where the events the drug user "sees" are completely different from those experienced by anyone else, and all the gradients in between.

Expressions like "haunted by the past," or "he lives in the past," or, better yet, "you should just leave the past behind" are frequently-used but often not-understood examples of describing this process of the individual who, for seemingly unknown reasons, is constantly stuck in or focused on negative drug-related past experiences instead of being focused on what is occurring right here and now.

A non-drug-related example would be a man who suffered greatly in a war   (shell shock[46]). After the war, he seems to get involuntarily pulled back into reliving that memory by similar experiences or people in his current environment.

[46]**shell shock -** a mental disorder caused by stress of active warfare.

This destructive "side effect" of constantly pulling the drug user's attention away from the present and placing it on past drug use is caused by both chemical and environmental triggers.

By triggers, we mean the action of something, either chemically or environmentally, "reminding" the drug user involuntarily of past similar experiences.

We will discuss both chemical and environmental triggers separately for ease of understanding, but remember that a drug user often isn't aware of the difference. Also remember that both chemically and environmentally triggered cravings can occur at the same time, which is often the case with people who have used drugs for extensive periods of time.

CHEMICALLY TRIGGERED DRUG CRAVINGS

CHEMICALLY TRIGGERED DRUG CRAVINGS

As mentioned earlier, a drug is any substance that when taken into the body may modify one or more of its functions. L. Ron Hubbard's definition has proven to be simpler and more accurate. The Narconon® program is based on Mr. Hubbard's research and breakthroughs in drug rehabilitation. His definition is:

"Drugs are essentially poisons. The degree they are taken determines the effect. A small amount acts as a stimulant. A greater amount acts as a sedative. A larger amount acts as a poison and can kill one dead. This is true of any drug. Each has a different amount at which it gives those results."

A small amount acts as a stimulant.

A greater amount acts as a sedative.

A larger amount acts as a poison and can kill one dead.

Despite what a person may think about drugs, the body identifies drugs as toxins or poisons as soon as they are taken.

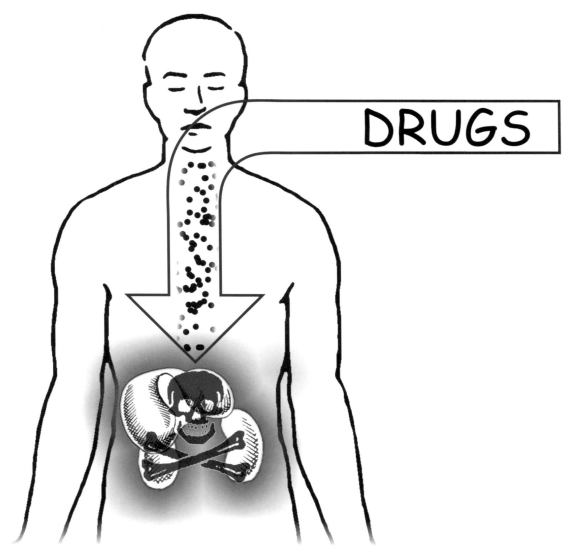

This causes the liver and kidneys to instantly begin breaking the drug down to allow it to be excreted[47] by normal bodily functions. The drugs or poisons are broken down into what are called "metabolites[48]," which are more easily eliminated from the body.

[47]**excreted -** eliminated from the body.
[48]**metabolite -** any substance involved in, or a product of, the organic processes in a cell or organism necessary for life.

Unfortunately, these metabolites are fat-bonding.

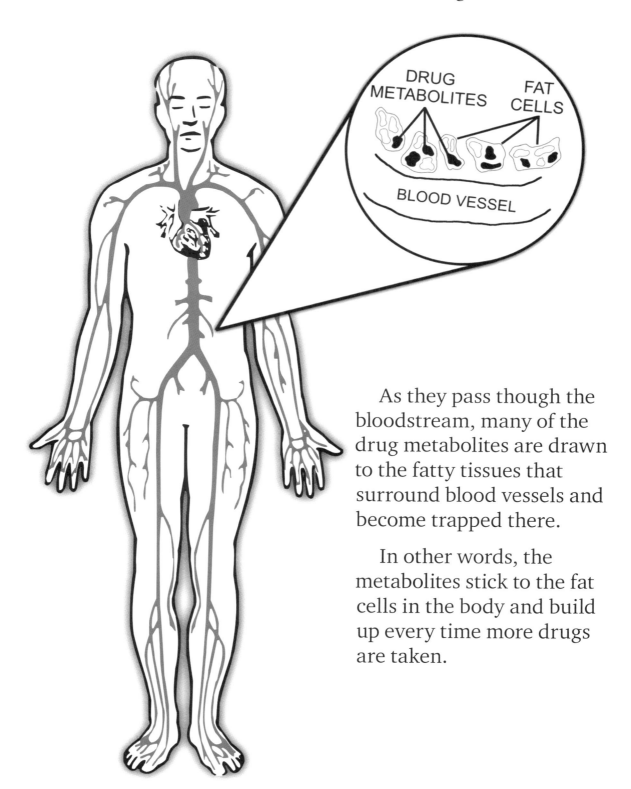

As they pass though the bloodstream, many of the drug metabolites are drawn to the fatty tissues that surround blood vessels and become trapped there.

In other words, the metabolites stick to the fat cells in the body and build up every time more drugs are taken.

This creates a "body burden" that may stay there for many years. Studies suggest that drug metabolites can affect the body's functioning for a very long time, even decades.

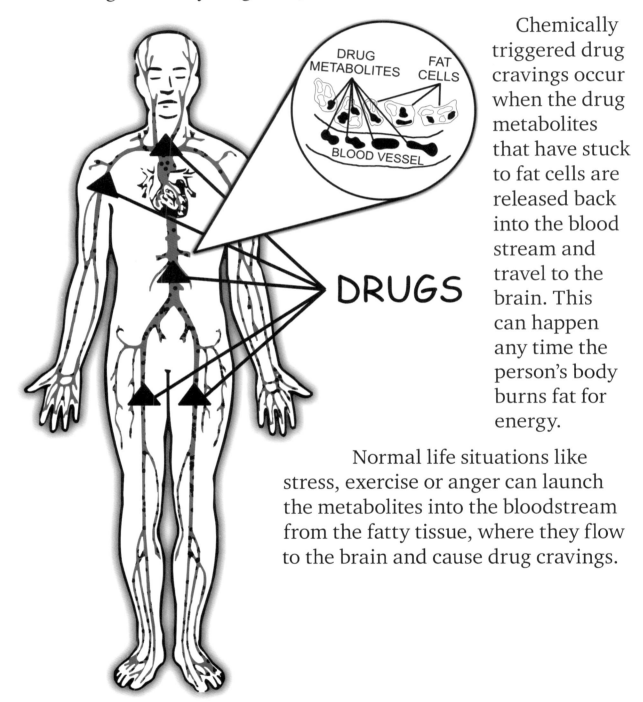

Chemically triggered drug cravings occur when the drug metabolites that have stuck to fat cells are released back into the blood stream and travel to the brain. This can happen any time the person's body burns fat for energy.

Normal life situations like stress, exercise or anger can launch the metabolites into the bloodstream from the fatty tissue, where they flow to the brain and cause drug cravings.

While one may have heard stories about individuals having "flashbacks[49]" from LSD[50], individuals who have used any psychoactive[51] drug can experience frequent and subtle drug "flashbacks" and can also have drug cravings for years after they have stopped taking the drugs.

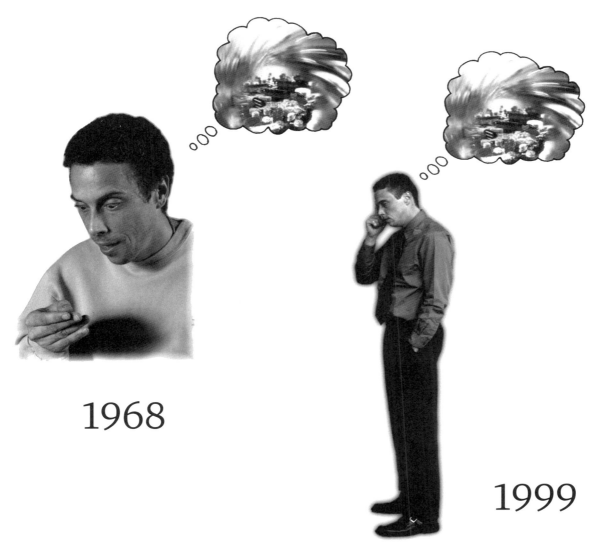

1968

1999

[49]**flashback** - an unexpected but vivid recurrence* of a past experience (especially a recurrence of the effects of an hallucinogenic** drug taken much earlier).
***recurrence** - happening again (especially at regular intervals).
****hallucinogenic** - capable of producing an illusionary (mistaken or false) perception.
[50]**LSD** - a powerful hallucinogenic drug.
[51]**psychoactive** - affecting the mind or mood or other mental processes.

To understand drug cravings, one needs to understand how we store memories and how they are sometimes recalled unexpectedly.

As we live life, we record mental image pictures of our experiences, which are "snap shots" of living, and store them for future reference.

This consecutive[52] record of mental image pictures is called a "time track." These "snap shots" or mental image pictures are actually full perception memories that include sight, sound, feelings, motion, decisions, conclusions, etc.

[52]**consecutive** - sequential; in regular succession without gaps.

A simple example of these mental image pictures and their recall is seen when a person smells something cooking in the kitchen and instantly identifies what it is.

The person can remember the smell to be that of cookies and remembers how much they loved it when their mom made them. If the person were to really focus their attention on the memory, they can almost taste the cookies as well.

This is due to the very detailed memory of cookies in the person's past, which again includes the sight of their mom's kitchen, the sounds of the pots clanging, the taste of the cookies and milk and the emotional feelings of joy and love they felt for their mom and the good feelings associated with eating cookies.

While this is a fond memory, keep in mind that it was brought on simply by the smell of something cooking in the kitchen.

Unfortunately, this works exactly the same way with drug memories. Every time a person uses drugs, he or she stores real life experiences (mental image pictures) of that drug use.

Drug-related memories, like every other memory, contain the thoughts, sights, sounds, feelings, emotions and decisions from the time the person was using the drug.

However, these memories are often very irrational[53] and highly emotional.

For example, when a drug that is stored in the fatty tissue is released back into the blood stream, it flows to the brain where it triggers or chemically reminds the person of the use of that type of drug in the past.

If the metabolite were from cocaine, the triggered memory would be that of using cocaine, or an emotional experience related to cocaine in some way.

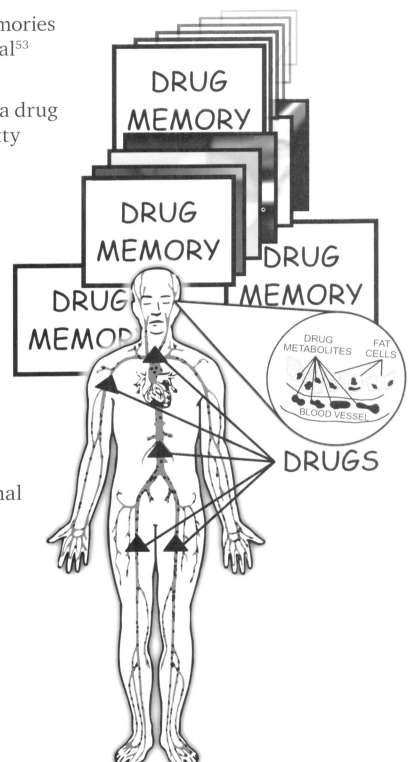

[53]**irrational -** not consistent with or using reason.

Here is a situation that many people find themselves in. A person abuses drugs and then, for good reason, decides to stop. He or she will decide to quit using drugs and attempt to get his or her life together. Suddenly, without warning, the person remembers times when he or she used drugs, places where drugs were purchased or the like, and then the former addict experiences a strong desire to use drugs again.

These memories also contain the physical and emotional pain and despair associated with the prior use of drugs.

When these memories are triggered, the person will re-experience the same pain and despair, to some degree, in the present. The individual feels bad, but doesn't know WHY. Again, this can occur at any time, regardless of what the person is doing. All that has to occur is for the metabolites of past drug use to be released back into the bloodstream and travel to the brain.

While in this state, the person can easily fall back into the pattern of addicted thinking, which is: "if you feel bad, take a drug or drink and you'll feel better."

This overall process of chemically triggered memories is commonly referred to as physical and emotional drug cravings. In spite of real and logical reasons he or she has to quit using drugs, the person involuntarily desires to use drugs again.

Without the total removal of these drug metabolites from the body, even an addict who has managed to come off drugs may experience these drug cravings, or chemically triggered drug memories, for years after quitting.

Drug cravings are the most common reason for relapse after typical substance abuse rehabilitation. When these cravings hit, former addicts who have been clean for months or years can suddenly find themselves back on the street using drugs, baffled by their failure to control themselves and their addiction.

Since addicts cannot find any logical reason for craving drugs, they will be completely mystified[54] as to why this is happening, and begin to experience feelings of hopelessness, despair and failure.

Each time this happens, it becomes harder for them to believe that addiction to drugs and alcohol can be conquered.

At some point, a drug addict knows that they need to stop using drugs, but at the same time they are aware that they can't stop thinking about them. Studies indicate that from the date of last use an addict may be affected by drug cravings for anywhere from five to forty years.

Let's review L. Ron Hubbard's definition of a "problem" as it applies to this aspect of addiction. A "problem" is: "the conflict arising from two opposing intentions"…"it's one thing versus another thing"…"It's intention versus counter-intention that worries the person."

[54]**mystified** - puzzled or bewildered.

Intention is defined in a standard dictionary as: "an idea or action that you intend to carry out." Counter-intention then is an intention or idea that one is going to do something which is counter to or against another intention.

There comes a point where the drug user realizes they have a very serious problem. He or she now knows that they must quit using drugs. They know their life is filled with problems because of their drug use and deeply desire or intend to stop using drugs.

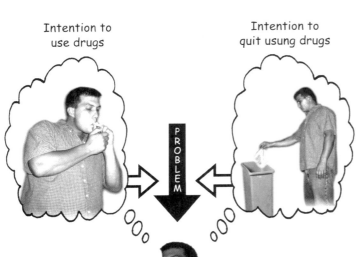

Intention to use drugs

Intention to quit usung drugs

Unfortunately, every time an addict tries to quit using drugs they experience involuntary drug cravings. This causes them to have an equally strong desire to use drugs again.

He or she is baffled as to what to do. As far as they are concerned, if there ever was a PROBLEM, this is IT.

ENVIRONMENTALLY TRIGGERED DRUG CRAVINGS

ENVIRONMENTALLY TRIGGERED DRUG CRAVINGS

Environmentally triggered craving are similar to chemically triggered cravings except the drug related memories or mental image pictures are environmentally triggered. That is, the person suddenly recalls past events triggered by events in the person's present environment.

Drug users will have traumatic[55] mental image pictures of drug use, and these pictures will contain not only the memories of the drug usage itself, but also the circumstances surrounding the drug use. Things like where the drugs were bought, who sold the drugs to them, how they felt about buying the drugs, and many more thoughts and feelings will be present in these mental image pictures.

A drug user also stores in his or her memory all the negative things they do while under the influence of drugs in these mental image pictures. Moments of pain and betrayal[56] mixed with moments of pleasure and bliss. All sensations experienced while under the influence of drugs are stored in these memories.

---

[55]**traumatic -** causing physical or especially psychological injury; psychologically painful.
[56]**betrayal -** the act or result of treason, treachery or aiding an enemy.

If a drug user is driving a car and passes a certain street, he or she may be reminded of trips to the drug dealer's house and experience again, to a certain degree, all the anxiety and stress related to that incident. If the person sees a liquor ad on a billboard, he or she can be reminded of drunken incidents and the associated pains or pleasures that were experienced at that time.

Once a drug user has used drugs for an extended period of time, he or she will have millions of subtle, and obvious, people, places and things in the environment that "remind" them or trigger the thought of drug use.

A drug user may watch TV and see actors acting out a scene about drinking and being drunk. As a result, this same drug user may suddenly find him or herself engulfed in negative memories of their own drunken ordeals.

An argument with a spouse can instantly remind the drug user of similar arguments they had while intoxicated.

Often, the strongest environmental triggers are those that are directly connected with the use of drugs.

For instance, if someone uses a straw to snort cocaine, then whenever the user sees a straw in a soft drink this triggering of drug-related memories can occur.

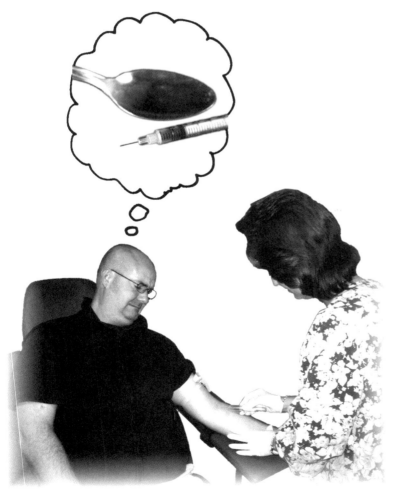

If the person uses a drug by injecting it into the veins with a needle, then each time he or she has blood drawn at the doctor's office may produce an overwhelming desire to get and use drugs.

As the "tools" of drug use are often straws, razors, hypodermic needles, shot glasses, mirrors, cigarette lighters, glass tubes and a whole assortment of other very common objects, the person can come into contact with on a day-to-day basis, the potential for the drug user to be constantly reminded of past drug use is staggering.

What this means for the person who is attempting to quit using drugs is that every day their attention can easily be involuntarily pulled away from what is going on in the present and become fixed on past drug- related memories.

Obviously, environmentally triggered cravings, just like chemically triggered cravings, are very distracting for the individual.

The person finds it hard to concentrate. They suffer from mood swings where they become upset or disturbed for seemingly unknown reasons. The person can "lose their train of thought" in mid-sentence and not remember what they were talking about. They can simply be driving to work and suddenly be thrown into the emotional struggle of their lives fighting the urge to immediately go get drugs and use them.

This process of automatic, environmentally triggered cravings is devastating and nightmarish for anyone attempting to leave drugs and alcohol behind.

We are reminded again of the mechanics of a problem. If a problem consists of intention versus counter-intention, then the drug user has absolutely encountered a severe problem.

Everything about the person's life indicates that they must stop using the drug, so their intention is to not use drugs again.

On the other hand, the person is constantly made to think of drug use or related experiences which is a counter-intention.

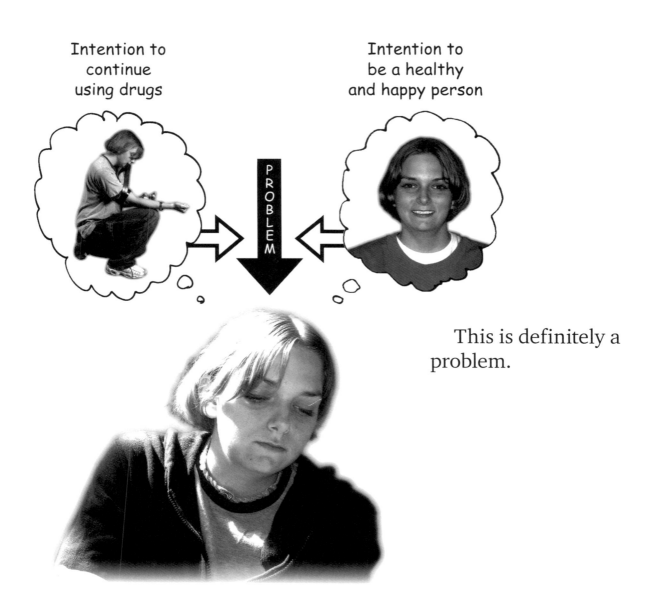

Intention to continue using drugs

Intention to be a healthy and happy person

PROBLEM

This is definitely a problem.

A drug user's existence is dominated by desires to become clean and stop using drugs so his or her quality of life will improve. That desire is continually opposed by an overpowering compulsion[57] to use drugs, which creates the indecision of not knowing how to stop this internal conflict.

This situation is a sinister trap. If drug users do not find an effective solution, they will remain enslaved for the rest of their lives, which is why many describe addiction as "incurable."

Drugs and other toxins lodged in the body can be flushed out and eliminated through a specific program developed by L. Ron Hubbard called the New Life Detoxification Program. This process is one of the key steps in the Narconon® drug and alcohol rehabilitation program, as it

effectively reduces the chemical triggers that cause drug cravings.

The Narconon program also contains study and exercises which help a person become less and less affected by the environmental triggers that cause drug cravings.

The Narconon drug and alcohol rehabilitation program achieves, on average, a very high success rate in people becoming permanently drug-free.

The preceding are only a few of the reasons why.

---

[57]**compulsion** - an irresistible impulse to say or do something that might be better left unsaid or undone.

PERSONAL VALUES

PERSONAL VALUES

Another problem that occurs with drug use is the gradual lowering of a person's morals[58] and personal values, which, in turn, lowers the drug user's most basic survival abilities.

We can start with the simple viewpoint that an addict is basically good. In other words, he or she wants to do the right thing and has a basic concept of right and wrong.

The basic concept of right and wrong referred to here is what is considered to be a moral code. L. Ron Hubbard defines a moral code as, "that series of agreements to which a person has subscribed to guarantee the survival of the group." A group can be a family, a company, a city or the entire human race.

An example of a common "moral code" in the United States, for instance, is the majority acceptance of the idea that it is OK to catch, kill and eat fish. As catching, killing and eating fish is commonly viewed as an acceptable method of surviving as a group, this is considered to be OK.

[58]**morals -** motivations and standards of conduct based on ideas of right and wrong.

However, it is not considered acceptable by the majority of people to catch, kill and eat an endangered species. As the majority of the United States population has not agreed that catching, killing and eating an endangered species is acceptable, then to do so would be a crime against the very moral codes of the United States. In fact, it is actually against the law and punishable by the country's judicial system.

The key thing to understand is that a moral code is strictly agreed-upon behavior and thus is, by definition, created by individual AGREEMENT.

When a person does something that is against their group's agreed-upon rules for survival, they have committed what we call an "overt act."

L. Ron Hubbard defines an overt act as, "an intentionally committed harmful act committed in an effort to resolve a problem."

For example, a drug user needs the drugs he or she has become addicted to, but doesn't have the money to buy them.

To solve this problem, the person frequently steals money from their parents.

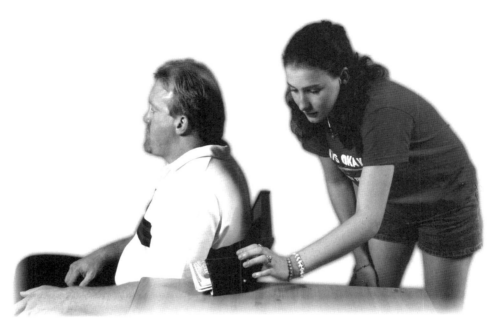

This is an overt act. The drug user knows that stealing money from their parents, or, for that matter, anyone else, is wrong but intentionally commits the act any way in an attempt at solving the problem of needing drugs.

Once the drug user commits an overt act they will immediately begin withholding this act from others. The action of actively withholding things from others is called a "withhold."

L. Ron Hubbard defines a "withhold" as follows:

"a withhold is an unspoken, unannounced transgression[59] against a moral code by which the person was bound"...

"a withhold is something that the person believes that if it is revealed it will endanger their self preservation"...

"a withhold is something the person did that he isn't talking about"...

"a withhold is restraining self from communicating"...

"a withhold is always the manifestation which comes after an overt is committed."

The person commits an overt act. He or she immediately considers that if this act were known, there would be negative, non-survival consequences as a result, so the person actively withholds this action from those who the person considers "mustn't know."

[59]**transgression** - the violation of a law or a duty or moral principle.

Remember that the act of withholding something is an action which requires energy and attention. One of the most destructive effects drug use has on the individual is the enormous amount of attention and energy the person must expend withholding the many overt or harmful actions they do from everyone around them.

Since the person has to hide more and more overt acts from those in their environment, those people they are withholding things from begin to represent pain and struggle to the drug user.

In addition to stealing from the family, the person has often lied to the family about things they have done to the family. They have also withheld many things from the family that they feel would hurt the family and ultimately themselves if the family found out.

Each time the drug user comes in contact with his or her family, he or she is reminded of these actions and must actively restrain themselves from telling the truth.

Can't we just talk about it?

This is one reason that the person will start to pull away from or be unable to face or confront those people, places and things they have committed overts against.

A young person tries drugs, knows it is wrong because their family has the agreement that drug use is wrong. The person must now withhold this act from his or her parents because of the fear of punishment of some kind.

This person will find it harder and harder to be around their parents and will often stay in their room or spend much of their time away from their house in an attempt at distancing themselves from those they have committed the overt against.

The drug user will also distance themselves from the family by becoming antagonistic[60] toward them, as this is another means of ultimately removing themselves from the family by cutting communication with them.

This is a common occurrence for drug users. Regardless of who the people they have harmed are, the addict will not be able to confront them, and will start to pull away from them.

The person lies to their boss by telling him they are sick when in actual fact they are suffering from a hangover from the previous night's party. As the person considers this an overt, he or she will begin to some degree to pull away from their employer as a result of the overt-withhold process.

[60]**antagonistic -** arousing hostility; in opposition to or resistant toward, incompatible.

A very recognizable action that usually follows the commission of an overt act is "justification."

L. Ron Hubbard defines justification as: "a social mechanism a person uses when he has committed an overt act and withheld it. It is a means by which a person can relieve himself of consciousness of having done an overt act by trying to lessen the overt. This is done by finding fault or displacing blame. It is explaining the most flagrant[61] wrongnesses. The reason overts are not overts to people are justifications."

L. Ron Hubbard further explains: "hence when a man or a woman has done an overt act, there usually follows an effort to reduce the goodness or importance of the target of the overt."

[61]**flagrant** - obviously and outrageously bad or offensive.

A person steals money from their parents to buy drugs. This person knows this is an overt or harmful act but will blame the parent for causing this because he is "always mean to me." The overt is stealing money. The target of the overt is the parent, since the parent is who the person committed the overt act against. The justifier is, "he's always mean to me" or "he deserves it because ..."

Regardless of the way the parent treats the person, the person still knows it is wrong to steal and deep down inside feels guilt and shame, despite attempts to make the parents responsible for his or her own misdeeds.

Parents often wonder why their child who is using drugs is constantly fighting with them and blaming their drug use on the family. This is merely the process of justifying the person's overts by attempting to lessen the target of the overt.

Unfortunately, there sometimes may be some truth in the "justifiers" the drug user is using against the family. This commonly causes the family to feel guilty over mishandlings of the past or family upsets. The drug user will use a remembered past event to JUSTIFY his or her own current wrong actions.

If the family is not aware of this process of justification, they will often concede[62] wrongly that the drug user is right, and that they, the family, are ultimately responsible for the person's using drugs.

[62]**concede** - to declare or admit, often reluctantly, the existence or reality or truth of.

The truth is, despite any responsibility the family might have for problems of the past, the drug user knows that drug use and the destructive actions that accompany drug use are not OK and that his or her drug use is not caused by their family. He or she is responsible for his or her own actions.

So we have a person committing overt or destructive actions against many people, places and things in their environment as a means of solving problems associated with drug use.

As this cycle continues, the person pulls away from more and more areas in their life they have committed overt actions against.

The person becomes antagonistic toward these areas as a further means of distancing themselves from these people, places and things.

The drug user will be seen to take less and less responsibility for these areas of their life. They won't actually participate in or help or be held accountable for even basic family survival issues such as food, shelter, etc.

The drug user often takes no responsibility for their work performance, place of employment or co-workers.

The person often takes no responsibility for community activities they should be involved in.

Ultimately, the drug user ends up taking no responsibility for practically anything.

Concurrently[63], this person's abilities to handle life and living diminish proportionately. Often, even providing their own food, clothing and shelter becomes overwhelming to the drug user and must be obtained from others who care for them.

Can I have some money for dinner?

[63]**concurrently -** at the same time; overlapping in duration.

What the drug user ends up achieving is lonely isolation and despair. They have exhausted the help of the only people in the person's life who really loved and cared for them.

By this stage, it is usually very apparent to the drug user that the solution that drugs offer is in actual fact a sinister lie, but due to the massive harmful effects drug use produces, the person finds him or herself trapped in addiction and unable to do anything about it.

That is when drug users often simply give up. They resign themselves to a life of depriviation and pain and await the end that inevitably[64] approaches.

---

[64]**inevitably** - in such a manner as could not be otherwise; unavoidably.

Whether experiencing a living death or on the verge of death itself, drug users are, at this point, at the end of the line.

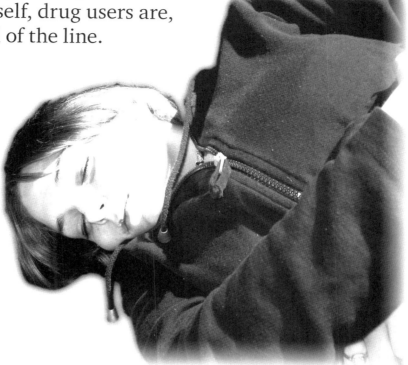

Fortunately, no matter how hopeless it may seem, the trap of addiction can be undone. Every day, people starting the Narconon® drug and alcohol rehabilitation program begin the process of rebuilding their lives and repairing the damages done by drug use.

There are methods utilized by the Narconon program to help the person get honest and straight as well as handle the abundance[65] of negative effects of drug use.

It is not easy, but those who have done or observed the Narconon drug and alcohol rehabilitation program know that people can stably[66] overcome addiction and lead happy and productive lives.

[65]**abundance -** the property of a more than adequate quantity
[66]**stably** - in a stable, fixed or unchanging manner.

SUMMARY

SUMMARY

It is important to note that drug or alcohol addiction is not just about the individual who is suffering from the physical and mental anguish and declining quality of life. It's about the families, loved ones, friends and community that surround the addict who also suffer, sometimes as much or more than the addicted person themselves. The amount of turmoil[67] that surrounds an addict's life can at first glance appear overwhelming, and where to begin to help an addict can be a perplexing[68] proposition at best.

Unfortunately, we in the addiction rehabilitation field as a whole have been derelict[69] in our duty to make drug and alcohol addiction understandable to the average person. It is, after all, the average person that is affected most by the plague of drug addiction. If anything, the information that has been disseminated[70] as well as many of the therapies that are being offered today on this subject has confused society about this problem. From this confusion has emerged[71] a false idea that drug and alcohol addiction can be effectively treated through the "magic pill" theory or the idea that someday there will be some "quick fix" solution for the problem of addiction. This has not been nor will it ever be the case. There is no pill that someone can take to overcome drug and alcohol addiction.

[67]**turmoil -** a disorderly disturbance or outburst.
[68]**perplexing -** lacking clarity of meaning; causing confusion.
[69]**derelict -** failing in what duty or obligation requires.
[70]**disseminated -** caused to become widely known; spread about.
[71]**emerged -** came into view from concealment; became known or apparent.

The information on addiction as contained in this book may seem new and revolutionary, but it is factual and appeals to common sense. It has been presented here in the hope that you, the reader, will be able to understand each of the component parts that begin and propel[72] forward the life cycle of addiction. Only then does it become apparent that all of the symptoms described in this material are treatable, and that there is real hope for successful recovery. The more one knows about the causes and symptoms of addiction, the clearer it becomes that substitute drugs, aversion[73] therapy, or any other rehabilitation methodology[74] that seeks to only mask these symptoms will prove unworkable in the end in most cases.

Over 35 years of experience in working with addicts, their friends and families have taught those who deliver the Narconon® drug and alcohol program that once a person understands addiction, they then experience renewed hope in resolving this problem. In addition to this, they realize that successfully treating these symptoms lies in nutritionally repairing the body and teaching the addict how to confront and solve problems while offering commonsense moral guidance and a systematic way for an addict to correct the negative situations that are left behind from an addicted life style. By understanding this, half of the battle in eliminating the problem of drug and alcohol addiction is already won. So when an addict is reaching and ready for help, selecting a rehabilitation program that embraces these ideals then becomes the next logical step to take.

[72]**propel** - to cause to move forward on onward.
[73]**aversion** - a feeling of intense dislike; distaste.
[74]**methodology** - the body of practices, procedures and rules used in a specific area of investigation.
[75]**manualized** - treated according to, or using the methods of, a standard reference text.
[76]**intervene** - get involved in, usually so as to hinder or halt an action.

The book you have just read is the first in a series that is being written to not only make you equally as informed as our nation's rehabilitation experts on this important subject but to also show you how to effectively and systematically help someone overcome the perils of addiction and get them on the road to a sober and satisfying life.

The Narconon drug and alcohol rehabilitation program is one of the most effective rehabilitation methods available today. Past and continuing studies show that the majority of Narconon program graduates achieve stably drug-free, ethical and productive lives. The Narconon program's drug and alcohol rehabilitation philosophy and methods were researched and developed by author, humanitarian and expert on improving the human condition, L. Ron Hubbard. The Narconon program's manualized[75] rehabilitation method systematically resolves each of the underlying factors of drug or alcohol addiction and teaches addicted individuals how to repair the damage done to their relationships and improve their quality of life in the recovery process.

The second book in this series will take you to the next step in helping someone overcome addiction and arm you with information and techniques that teaches one how family members, loved ones or friends can intervene[76] to stop an addict's destructive behavior and support their decision to seek help.

Drug and alcohol addiction can be overcome. By reading this book, you have started the process. For additional help or information, contact a Narconon center today.

GLOSSARY

GLOSSARY

abstinence - the act or practice of refraining from indulging an appetite

abundance - the property of a more than adequate quantity

amino acid - organic compounds which combine to form proteins.

antagonistic - arousing hostility; in opposition to or resistant toward, incompatible.

anxiety - a vague, unpleasant emotion experienced in anticipation of some (usually poorly defined) misfortune.

aversion - a feeling of intense dislike; distaste.

betrayal - the act or result of treason, treachery or aiding an enemy.

catastrophic - extremely harmful, bringing physical or financial ruin.

cause - to make happen or occur; to be the origin of something.

cirrhosis - a chronic disease interfering with the normal functioning of the liver; the primary cause is chronic alcoholism.

cocaine - a powerfully addictive stimulant that directly affects the brain.

compulsion - an irresistible impulse to say or do something that might be better left unsaid or undone.

concede - to declare or admit, often reluctantly, the existence or reality or truth of.

concurrently - at the same time; overlapping in duration.

confront - to deal with (something unpleasant) directly, without fear or uncertainty .

conscious - intentionally conceived; having awareness of surroundings and sensations and thoughts.

consecutive - sequential; in regular succession without gaps.

craving - an intense desire for some particular thing. consuming desire.

deficiency - lack of an adequate quantity or number; the state of needing something that is absent or unavailable.

depressant - capable of depressing physiological or psychological activity or response by a chemical agent.

derelict - failing in what duty or obligation requires.

derivation - an explanation of the historical origins of a word or phrase

disseminated - caused to become widely known; spread about.

emerged - came into view from concealment; became known or apparent.

euphoric - characterized by an exaggerated feeling of well- being or happiness.

excreted - eliminated from the body.

flagrant - obviously and outrageously bad or offensive.

flashback - an unexpected but vivid recurrence of a past experience (especially a recurrence of the effects of an hallucinogenic drug taken much earlier).

fundamental - serving as an essential component; involving basic facts or principles.

hallucinogenic - capable of producing an illusionary (mistaken or false) perception.

heroin - a highly addictive narcotic derived from the opium poppy plant.

immune system - a system that protects the body from foreign substances and disease-causing organisms by producing the immune response.

indecision - doubt concerning two or more possible alternatives or courses of action.

indulging - enjoying to excess; giving satisfaction to.

inevitably - in such a manner as could not be otherwise; unavoidably.

inorganic - lacking the properties characteristic of living organisms.

intervene - get involved in, usually so as to hinder or halt an action.

irrational - not consistent with or using reason.

LSD - a powerful hallucinogenic drug.

magnitude - greatness, in reference to influence or effect.

manualized - treated according to, or using the methods of, a standard reference text.

marijuana - a drug consisting of the dried leaves of the hemp plant; smoked or chewed for euphoric effect

mass- marketing - the act or business of promoting sales of a product to a large number of people, as by advertising or packaging.

metabolite - any substance involved in, or a product of, the organic processes in a cell or organism necessary for life.

methamphetamine - a powerfully addictive stimulant that affects the central nervous system.

methodology - the body of practices, procedures and rules used in a specific area of investigation.

mineral - an inorganic element, such as calcium, used in the metabolism of human beings, animals and plants.

misinformation - information that is incorrect.

monotony - the quality of boring sameness and lack of variety.

morals - motivations and standards of conduct based on ideas of right and wrong.

mystified - puzzled or bewildered.

Narconon® drug and alcohol rehabilitation program - a non- traditional residential drug and alcohol rehabilitation program. Over 70% of Narconon program graduates remain drug-free.

nervous system - the sensory and control apparatus, consisting of a network of nerve cells, that regulates the body's responses to input, especially from the environment.

nutrient - any substance that can be metabolized by an organism to give energy and build tissue.

organic - of or relating to or derived from living organisms.

peer - a person who is of equal standing with another in a group.

perception - becoming aware of something via the senses.

perplexing - lacking clarity of meaning; causing confusion.

physiological - of or consistent with an organism's normal functioning.

poison - any substance that causes injury or illness or death of a living organism.
propel - to cause to move forward or onward.
psychoactive - affecting the mind or mood or other mental processes.
recurrence - happening again (especially at regular intervals).
refraining - not doing something, resisting.
relapse - failure to maintain a higher state.
sedative - a drug that reduces excitability and calms a person.
sensation - the faculty through which the external world is perceived and understood.
shell shock - a mental disorder caused by stress of active warfare.
side effect - a secondary and usually adverse (undesirable) effect of a drug or therapy.
stably - in a stable, fixed or unchanging manner.
stimulant - a drug that temporarily quickens some physiological process.
tolerance - the power or capacity of an organism to withstand, and function in, unfavorable environmental conditions
transgression - the violation of a law or a duty or moral principle.
traumatic - causing physical or especially psychological injury; psychologically painful.
turmoil - a disorderly disturbance or outburst.
value - the quality (positive or negative) that renders something desirable or valuable.
vitamins - any of a group of organic substances essential to normal metabolism.
withdrawal - the physiological and mental symptoms that accompany the stopping of taking an addictive drug.